Bella —

I hope you love this story, but remember:

Don't take the Pillow!

MEDISON

PILLOWS
FOR YOUR
PRISON CELL

PILLOWS
FOR YOUR
PRISON CELL

MARK D. BULLARD

BrainSquall

Mark D. Bullard
BrainSquall Books
P.O. Box 4736
Rollingbay, WA 98061

Published 2014 by BrainSquall Books

Printed in the United States of America

17 16 15 14   1 2 3 4

ISBN: 978-0-991162-40-6

Library of Congress Control Number: 2013956194

To Elle, the Bride of my youth.

Your hair got my attention first,
your wit and wisdom kept it.
Through many years of best and worst,
your love for me reflected.
That no matter where I go,
no matter what I write,
Your love for me will be there still,
through every day and night.

Thank you.

PROLOGUE

AMIR WAS PLAYING on the floor with his little brother when the door opened and his father walked in.

"Papa!" the two boys yelled as they jumped up and ran to him in the doorway. Amir, six, got there first and gave his father a big hug. Mamluk, who was only three, caught up and joined the hug. The man picked up the two boys, one in each arm, and looked back and forth at their two smiling faces.

"I love you two." Then he took in a deep breath. "What is that wonderful smell?" he asked.

Amir replied, "Mama is making lamb stew."

"She is? I love lamb stew, but we don't have that every day. What's the special occasion?" asked his father.

"Umm, your birthday?" proposed Amir.

"Is it my birthday today?" asked his father.

"Mama said it's your birthday. Are you teasing me? It's your birthday. I know it is because mama got the Jar down," said Amir.

"Well, if mama got the Jar down, it must be somebody's birthday, and it might as well be mine!" said his father.

Amir squirmed out of his father's arm and landed on the ground. "Mama! Papa is teasing me. It is his birthday, right?" he shouted.

Just at that moment, his mother came in from the kitchen and looked first at Amir. "You don't have to shout, dear, and yes, it is his birthday." She looked at her husband and smiled. "Happy birthday, my love."

Amir's father set Mamluk down and embraced his wife. "Thank you, Love. That stew smells so good. I will never grow tired of it. Thank you for making it."

"Thank you for making it possible," said Mother. She then returned to the kitchen to finish preparing the special dinner.

"All right, boys, will you help me get the table ready

for dinner? Amir, will you please get the bowls and put them out?"

"Yes, Papa," replied Amir.

Father then continued, "Mamluk, please get four spoons, and put one in each bowl."

"Yes, Papa," replied Mamluk.

Father then went into the kitchen and came back with the kettle of stew, which he set on the table. Mother followed him out with some warm, freshly baked bread. After blessing the meal, he poured some lamb stew into each of their bowls, and Mother cut up the bits of lamb and vegetables in Mamluk's bowl into very small pieces while Father did the same for Amir.

Father took a bite and moaned with approval. He finished the bite and said, "Love, I swear you make it better every year." After everyone had finished their servings, the boys asked for more.

Father looked at the two boys. "I know you boys are young, but I want you to learn something important. Mama and I gave you enough lamb stew so that you would be well fed. Mama loves to hear that you like it so much that you want more. And I want more too because I liked it so much. But remember that the desire for more is insatiable. That means that it never quits."

Amir protested, "But I only want a little bit more."

"I understand, Son, and I want to give you more. But it's even more important to me that you learn this lesson. It's important to be a master over your wants. Speaking of wants, who wants to get that Jar down?"

The children cleared the table, and Father grabbed the Jar.

"What is this, Mamluk?" he asked.

"The Jar," Mamluk replied.

"That's right. And what is in it, Amir?" he asked.

"Money!" shouted Amir.

"That's right. And what is it for, boys?" he asked while looking at both of them.

"For buying a country," said Mamluk.

"Well, that's close, dear; it's for buying some land out *in* the country—some land of our own," said Father.

"Yeah, so we can have our own sheeps and chickens!" said Amir.

"And flowers," added Mamluk.

"That's exactly right. So we can have our own sheep, chickens, cows, vegetables, honey, and grain," said Father.

"And flowers," added Mother.

"And flowers," concluded Father.

"Papa?" asked Amir.

"Yes?" replied Father.

"When are we going to get our land in the country?" asked Amir.

"Well, that's why we get the Jar down every birthday. We count the money that we've added every day since the last birthday, and then we add a little extra. Let's count it," said Father. With that, he upended the Jar. Gold and silver coins came out of the Jar and landed in a pile on the table. Father added two gold coins to the pile, and together as a family, they counted out the money.

"Well, we are more than halfway there! We've been saving since before Amir was born, and we only have about five years to go. If we keep it up, we'll be there soon," said Father.

"Papa, why can't we just get it now? Why do we have to wait?" asked Amir.

"That's a good question, Amir. The answer is that we don't have enough money yet," said Father.

"Why don't you just get some more money from work?" asked Amir.

"I will. Every day that I work, I bring home money. Some of it goes to pay for our home, and our food, and our clothes, but I always put some in the Jar."

"I wish you could just work a whole bunch and get all the money, and then we could just get our land in the country right now!" said Amir.

"Me too, my boy, but that's not the way it works. We have to be patient. But if I continue to work hard and you and your brother help Mama by taking care of the things we have, we can save more money every year. Before we know it, we'll have enough to buy that land and get those animals, and our dream will come true."

His father leaned down to look at Amir face-to-face.

"Just watch," he said with a wink.

•I•

THE DECISION

THE DAY HAD STARTED like every other. Amir woke up to a kiss from his father, who was heading off to work. "I love you," said Father.

"I love you too, Papa," replied Amir in the middle of a big stretch. He got ready for school, gave his mother a kiss and a goodbye hug, and did the same for his little brother.

That afternoon as he walked home from school, he and his friend were pretending to be soldiers. They were marching to their own cadence and trying to keep serious expressions on their faces, but every time they looked at one another, they started laughing. As they came around the corner to the street they both lived on, Amir saw a commotion around his house. His eyebrows furrowed, and his head tilted as he tried to imagine what could be going on. He started running toward his house and looked back to wave goodbye to his friend. As he approached the house, his mouth fell open. His aunt was standing outside the house rocking his sleeping brother on her shoulder while tears streamed down from her swollen eyes. His uncle was standing next to her. Amir had never trusted his father's brother. It felt like the man did everything out of duty and nothing out of love. When he saw Amir approaching, he spread his arms out between Amir and the front door of the house and stepped toward Amir. His uncle's face was very serious. "Amir..." he started.

But Amir ducked under his arms and ran through

the open door. In the middle of the floor lay his father, surrounded by his mother and some people Amir didn't know. There were rags and towels soaked in blood all around his father. His uncle followed Amir inside and told him that his father had been in a bad accident at work and that he was not expected to live much longer. Amir did not take his eyes off of his father.

Suddenly, his father's eyes opened and looked over at Amir. Amir moved closer.

"I love you…" his father uttered.

To which Amir replied, "I love you too, Papa." Big tears streamed down Amir's face, even though he tried not to cry.

Then his father continued, "Just… watch." He closed his eyes and breathed his last breath.

Amir fell to the floor, wailing and pounding it with his fists. His uncle grabbed him from behind and lifted him up. "Amir…" he said.

But Amir wriggled out of his arms and ran out the door. He sprinted down the dusty street, tears burning his eyes and streaming down his face.

Almost ten years later, Amir walked down the same street. Now sixteen, tears were a thing of the past, especially with Mamluk walking beside him. "I can't believe she's doing this," Amir muttered.

"What?" asked Mamluk.

"Nothing, just shut up and keep up with me," responded Amir a little louder.

"Can't believe she's doing what?" said Mamluk.

"I told you: it's nothing. Now shut up and keep up," said Amir, who was walking quickly because the only shirt he owned was hardly enough to keep him warm against the morning breeze.

"I think it's good to buy the chicken for Father's birthday," suggested Mamluk.

"Of course you do. You always agree with Mom," said Amir. "Plus, you just want to eat chicken. All you really care about is yourself."

Mamluk responded, "Mama loves us. She wants us

to celebrate. She hates to see us working so hard and missing school and everything."

"Well, that's great because now we're going to have to work even harder anyway," said Amir.

"Why?" said Mamluk.

Amir abruptly stopped walking and turned to face his brother directly. He shouted, "Because now the Jar is empty, you idiot!" Amir reached into his pocket and pulled out the five coins his mother had given him that morning. "*These* are all that is left of Father's dream for us. That's it. After today, we'll have nothing left."

"Maybe that's what was best for us in the long run," said Mamluk.

"No, that's what was best for us in the short run. You and Mom are always thinking about today, never about tomorrow," countered Amir.

"Well, today is Father's birthday, and we need to celebrate," said Mamluk.

"And tomorrow we'll have nothing if we buy that chicken today," said Amir resolutely.

"Oh yeah, well Mama told me that Father always

said, 'Just watch,' and she believes something good is right around the corner," said Mamluk.

"But he didn't mean, 'Sit back and do nothing and just watch.' He meant, 'Get out there and do everything you can, and *then* just watch what happens,'" Amir reasoned. "And he also said, 'The desire for more is insatiable.' But all you want is more and more. And Mama doesn't want to say 'No' to you."

"Well, I like Mama," said Mamluk.

"You like what she does for you," mumbled Amir under his breath as he turned toward the market and returned to a brisk walk. Then, loud enough for Mamluk to hear, "Just keep up with me."

They arrived at the market to find a pageant of colors, people, smells, and sights. Stalls dripping with brightly colored fabrics, ornamental beads, lamps, and teapots lined the narrow paths. The smells of spices, flowers, fresh fruits, and vegetables filled the air. Old and young, men and women, wealthy and poor were all there to acquire, to see, and to share in the experience. Normally, the boys relished the opportunity to walk through the whole market and soak up all the possibilities, even if they couldn't afford any of them.

Amir's favorite stall was the one stuffed with beautiful pillows of all sizes, shapes, and colors. The vendor was a kind man who always showed Amir the latest addition to his collection. Amir had been visiting this stall for years and had noticed early on a young girl who usually hid behind the booth. She looked roughly his age, and he learned from the vendor that she was his daughter and that she was very shy. The vendor's wife had died a few years earlier, and the daughter came to the market with him on market days, and helped him make and embellish the pillows every other day. Over the years, Amir's interest in pillows never waned, but it was no longer his only reason for stopping by that booth. The daughter had grown into a lovely young woman, and Amir had noticed. In fact, in the previous week's visit to the market, he had spent the better part of the morning learning about pillows. He asked about how the tassels were attached, where the fabric came from, how they were stuffed—more than any normal 16-year-old boy would care to know.

On this trip to the market, however, Amir went straight to the rice vendor.

"What? You're not going to see the pillow princess?" taunted Mamluk.

"Shut up!" said Amir.

After buying the week's supply of rice and beans, the brothers arrived at the chicken vendor.

"Hi there, boys. I haven't seen you or your mother in quite a while. What can I get for you?"

"We'd like half a chicken, please," said Amir.

"Only half? Last year you boys bought a whole chicken from me every week. What's wrong?" pried the butcher.

"Just half a chicken this time, please," repeated Amir.

"Okay, that'll be five coins," replied the butcher.

The words hit Amir like bricks. "What? It was always three coins before. We only have three coins left. What happened?"

The butcher started off rather quickly, "Well, Son, perhaps you've heard about the drought?" But when he saw the look in Amir's eyes, he changed course. "Look,

I'm really sorry about your father and all. I can give you a dozen eggs for three coins."

Amir was choking as he said, "My mom really wanted the chicken."

Just then, he heard a familiar voice from behind him. "I'll buy the chicken for the boys."

Amir turned around quickly to find the pillow vendor standing there. "Sir, I very much appreciate your generosity, but we cannot accept it."

"Please. I know today is an important day for your family. Allow me to give you this gift," said the vendor.

Amir closed his eyes for a second, took a breath, then reopened them. "No. Thank you very much, sir. But I must say 'No.'"

The vendor tilted his head down and looked into Amir's eyes. Amir looked at the ground, and the vendor lifted his head back up. "I understand. Blessings to you and your family." And he walked away toward his stall.

Amir pulled the last three coins from his pocket and exchanged them for the eggs.

"I hate eggs," winced Mamluk.

"Shut up," said Amir.

"You shut up," said Mamluk as he reached over toward Amir to shove him. As he did, Amir turned to leave the stall, and Mamluk's hand collided with the egg basket. All but one of the eggs toppled out of the basket and onto the hard, dusty earth at their feet. Amir watched each of the eggs as they fell through the air then one by one collided violently with the ground. He then snapped his head back up to lock his eyes on his brother. Mamluk's lips were pursed, but he could see in Amir's eyes that he was not safe.

Amir reached into the basket, grabbed the remaining egg, and threw it at Mamluk with all of his might. Ten years of frustration and fear exploded out of the two boys in fists, feet, elbows, and knees. Amir repeatedly hit Mamluk with his bigger, stronger, faster fists while the younger brother kicked, kneed, bit, and scratched in retaliation. The pain of the blows from his little brother's knee in Amir's side fueled his arms and tightened his fists. He could see blood running from his brother's nose and his eyes swelling, but he couldn't stop his fists until he heard a woman's voice coming from the crowd that had gathered around the boys.

"Stop! Please stop!"

Amir stopped for a moment and looked up to find the source of the voice. It was the pillow vendor's daughter. She stood, staring at Amir, with tears streaming down her face. "Please don't do that."

As soon as he saw her face and realized who had spoken, he immediately looked down at the ground then at his brother, who was wiping blood from his nose and a cut over his eye. Both boys were covered in blood, eggs, and dust. Amir stood up, shaking his head back and forth, then looked at the crowd of people that had formed around him. He could see disapproval in the women's eyes and disappointment in the men's.

Amir nudged his brother with his foot. "Let's go." He couldn't bear to look at the girl again, but he was looking for the rice and beans. They were gone, most likely stolen during the fray. At this, he let out a string of obscenities and threw a punch at his brother, who saw it coming, ducked out of the way, and retorted with his own curses.

Amir began to walk in the opposite direction of the girl, and his little brother followed at a safe distance. As they approached the exit, Amir suddenly stopped and looked to one side. Mamluk stopped and looked but didn't see what his brother saw. He then looked back at Amir, who continued staring intently down the aisle. Mamluk slowly approached his brother to discover the object of his interest.

All of a sudden, Amir started running in the direction he had been staring. Mamluk ran up to the spot where his brother had been standing and then saw for himself. A butcher had fresh chickens hanging in front of his stall, 50 paces away. Mamluk slowly followed Amir while looking at the stalls on either side of him.

A moment later he heard some yelling ahead of him, and out of nowhere, Amir came barreling past him with a chicken under his arm, yelling, "RUN!"

•2•

THE CONSEQUENCE

THE COURTROOM was uncomfortably warm. Though it was cool outside and the two windows were open, there was not sufficient airflow to provide relief to the judge, prosecutors, suspects, witnesses and observers that packed the room. A ray of sunlight shone through the window and slowly made its way across the floor as Amir and Mamluk waited their turn. The judge sat behind a large desk on a raised platform at the front of the room. There were large men guarding each of the entrances to the room and a scribe noting all of the actions of the judge and responses of the other parties in the room. The two boys sat on a bench in a row of accused men, facing the front of the courtroom. One man was accused of murder, two were accused of assaulting another man, but the rest of them were all in there for the same reason: theft. Their hands and feet were shackled, and a single chain tied the four shackles together on each man. The boys' mother sat in the crowd behind them, watching, waiting, and praying.

Amir could hear children playing outside and closed his eyes. For a moment, he was six again, running, playing, and laughing with his father. They were running around in the grass near a lake they would visit in the summer. After chasing their dad through the fields, they splashed into the water after him, all the while screaming and laughing. He could feel the sunlight warming his body as its path crossed his seat. Amir's short-lived joy was interrupted by the sound of his name.

"Amir and Mamluk were found stealing chickens at the market," said a large man at the front of the room as he cocked his head and waved his hand, beckoning them forward.

The judge now looked up from some papers on his desk to look at the boys for the first time. One of the guards grabbed Amir abruptly and shoved him into the open space in front of the judge's desk. Mamluk was shoved forward in the same manner, and they stood together in the patch of sunlight in the middle of the room.

The heat of the sun was warm on their bodies, but the low, slow voice of the judge sent shivers down their spines.

"Are you a chicken thief?" he said, folding his arms, leaning forward on the desk in front of him, and fixing his eyes first on Amir.

Amir glanced quickly up at the judge, then looked straight down at his feet. "No, sir."

The judge held up a piece of paper. "But my report says ten witnesses verified you stole a chicken from the market just yesterday."

"Yes, sir."

"Then you *did* steal a chicken?"

"Yes, sir," replied Amir, "but I've never done it before and..."

"Once a chicken thief, always a chicken thief," interrupted the judge. Then he looked at Mamluk. "And you? Are you a chicken thief?"

"No," said Mamluk, as he shot a look at his brother. "*He* is."

The judge lifted his sheet of paper again. "And yet I have multiple witnesses who saw you run alongside him, blocking people from catching him as you ran out of the market. If the guards had not caught you, I have no doubt that you would be at home right now, enjoying that chicken with your thief of a brother."

"But it wasn't my idea," said Mamluk.

"Silence!" ordered the Judge. He took a deep breath, pursing his lips while thinking for a moment. He folded his hands on the bench, looked down, and asked the boys, "Do you know the penalty for stealing?"

"No, sir," the boys murmured.

"The penalty for stealing is one year of hard labor."

Mamluk opened his mouth to complain further of the injustice, but Amir interrupted him, "Your Honor, this is my fault. It was my decision, and I should pay the price, not my brother."

"You're right," said the judge, speaking to Amir as he looked at Mamluk. Then he turned his gaze briefly to Amir. "I will double your sentence." Mamluk looked at his brother disdainfully, while the judge watched Mamluk's every move, and then the judge added, "And I will reduce your brother's to six months."

"What?" protested Mamluk.

"Silence, or I'll make it six years," ordered the judge through closed teeth. He leaned forward on his desk and lowered his voice. "You will carry out your sentence at The Mill."

At the sound of the words *The Mill*, their mother let out a scream from the back of the courtroom. She begged the judge, "Please, don't do this! They're good boys."

Amir felt a wave of shame over his body as tears escaped his eyes. Mamluk's face was red hot as he stood there, shaking his head back and forth, clenching his fists.

The judge motioned for the guards to remove the boys, and then he looked at papers on his table as the large man announced the next case.

Their mother looked at her boys. Mamluk was in a rage, yelling obscenities at his brother and the guards who were roughly dragging him out of the room. In his fury, he never looked back to see his mother. Another guard grabbed Amir firmly and led him away, but he looked back at his mother. She couldn't hear him, but she could read his lips as he said, "I'm sorry."

The brothers would go to The Mill in the morning, and so they had a night to ponder the destination that awaited them. Like everyone in their country, Amir and Mamluk had heard of The Mill their whole lives but actually knew very little about it. One thing they did know: no one sent there had ever come back.

A friend of Amir's at school had an uncle sentenced to five years at The Mill ten years ago, and no one had heard from him since. His story was a common one. One year. Five years. Ten years. It didn't seem to matter. No one ever left The Mill. Rumors abounded, but no one knew for sure what happened there. They just knew it wasn't good.

That night, Amir and Mamluk did not even look at each other, let alone talk to one another.

•3•
THE MILL

I T WAS STILL DARK when the guards awoke the boys the next morning, but by the time they arrived at The Mill, the sun was coming up. It was just above the entrance, shining directly in their eyes as they approached. The stone wall of The Mill grew taller and taller, eventually eclipsing the sun as they approached until it was like a sheer cliff in front of them, windowless and featureless apart from a small, black door at its base. The door opened, and two men dressed in black uniforms emerged from the darkness and yanked the boys out of the light, into a dark, dusty room within.

It took a moment for Amir's eyes to adjust to the dim interior light, and while they did, his ears tuned in to a faint interior buzzing sound. The sound reminded him of the whirring buzz of locusts, and he could feel it as much as hear it.

Is it in the walls? he wondered with a chill as he looked around.

There was nothing in the room aside from the two guards, who had retired and were standing at attention on alternate sides of an interior door on the opposite side of the room. Their uniforms were all black, with no visible markings, different from the grey and red uniforms of the police and guards who had handled them in the jail and courthouse.

Amir looked at Mamluk. Mamluk was staring at the floor, clenching his jaw so tightly that Amir could see the blood vessels on the side of his head popping out. Amir started to say, "Mamluk," when the internal door opened and another man entered through the doorway. Both boys immediately looked over at him.

The man in the doorway had the same black uniform but with the addition of markings on his shoulder and chest that suggested he was a superior. This assumption was confirmed when he barked an order: "To their cells." The two guards immediately grabbed the boys and pushed them through the door into the long hallway. They began a journey down one long, windowless hallway after another, up countless steps and through countless doors. Each hallway looked identical to every other: the floors were stone, the walls were stone, the ceiling was an arch of stones. There were heavy, windowless, metal doors lining the halls, suffocating any sound that might be sealed behind them. As they got deeper and deeper into The Mill, the churning, whizzing locust sound grew stronger, as if the walls themselves were buzzing.

After what felt like an eternity of walking, the lead guard and Mamluk turned left at an intersection, went through a door into a stairwell, and disappeared.

Amir's guard led him to the right, down yet another hall.

What just happened? Are we being separated? Amir thought to himself.

He cursed himself, and overwhelmed with guilt, he regretted that he never told Mamluk he was sorry. Suddenly, the guard stopped at a door and opened it.

Amir blurted out, "Where are they taking my brother?"

"Forget him." The guard heaved Amir into the room, and slammed the door shut. Amir fell to the ground and heard the sound of steel sliding against steel as the guard locked him in.

Amir lay on the floor in a state of shock, his mind spinning. It had never occurred to him that they would be separated. In fact, he had been dreading the idea of sharing a cell with his brother, who was obviously, and quite rightly, Amir thought, mad at him. Would he ever see him again? What would Mamluk say to their mother if he got out first? Would they ever get out?

Amir tried to get up on his knees and stand, but the

floor felt like it was tilting so violently beneath him that he lost his balance, fell back to his knees, and promptly threw up. He rolled over on his side and passed out.

Sometime later, he woke up to the sound of steel sliding on steel as the door was unlocked. He sat up, and though his head was still spinning, he did not lose his balance this time. The door opened, and in walked two men wearing the all-black prison uniform. They stood at perfect attention on either side of the door, staring into space with no expression on their faces.

"Please stand for His Highness, the Supreme Commander of The Mill, Hasec."

Amir slowly rose to his feet, trying to maintain balance by steadying himself against the wall. A short, sturdy man dressed in black pants and a bright red coat, decorated with tassels on his shoulders and ribbons and medals on his chest, stepped into the cell. He had thick, jet-black hair and thick eyebrows that jutted out over dark, piercing eyes, which looked first at Amir then at the mess on the floor next to him.

"I see you've had difficulty adjusting to your new

surroundings." He then looked at one of his men. "Would you please call a cleaner in here right away?" Then he looked at the other man. "And would you please remove these shackles?" he said, nodding toward Amir.

As the guard removed the shackles, Amir took stock of his surroundings. His eyes, now well-adjusted to the darkness, darted around the dimly lit room. It was roughly square, with stone floor, stone walls, and an arched stone ceiling like the hallways. The only breaches in the stone were the heavy metal door and pipes in the floor under an unusual contraption in the corner of the room. Aside from the contraption and the three people, there was nothing else in the room.

After surveying the entire room, Amir rubbed his wrists while turning his attention back to the contraption in the corner. It was a mess of pulleys and lines and wheels and bars, with ropes going down through the floor. Amir liked mechanical things, so he tried to imagine its purpose. Then it occurred to him!

Hasec had been studying Amir carefully and could

see the realization in his eyes. "I know what you're thinking," he said. "It's not a torture device." He walked over to it and continued, "No, it's quite the opposite. In fact, it is your means to freedom."

While he said that, the first guard returned with another person who promptly cleaned up the mess on the floor and left the cell. The two guards then remained at attention on either side of the door.

Upon hearing the word "freedom," Amir relaxed a little and took a few steps closer to the machine. "What do you mean?" he asked.

Hasec smiled faintly. "Well, as you know, this is a mill." He slowly lowered his voice, drawing Amir closer to the machine as he did so. "You can't see the grain. It's in another room. But when you sit here, like this—" He sat on the seat in the middle of the machine. "—and put your feet here and here, and your hands here and here, you can move these bars like this. Your work grinds the grain in the other room below."

Amir took a big breath and nodded his head, then looked up at the pulleys in the beam above and down at the ropes and chains that disappeared down into the floor. His eyes darted around as he took in all of the moving parts and gears.

"See? It's not that bad," said Hasec as he slowly moved his arms and legs back and forth, causing wheels to spin and pulleys to pull all around him. Hasec slowed down and allowed the machine to come to a rest.

"When you stole that chicken," he began as he eased off the machine and moved closer to Amir, "you made a bad decision. And that decision brought you here. But this is not a prison. No, a prison is a place of punishment." He let the last word hang in the air.

"This," he said, pointing at the machine, "is a place of redemption..."

Then he looked directly at Amir as his brow furrowed again, "...through service."

"You made a bad decision. But now you have the opportunity to pay back your debt to society. Your work will provide grain to your fellow citizens. Everyone will be better off for the work that you do. And that's not all. You get to provide for your mother too." At this, Amir's eyes grew bigger. He took a step back and looked down. Hasec was watching him closely and stepped forward, lowering his head to catch Amir's eyes.

"Yes, Amir. When you and your brother were sent here to The Mill, your mother was placed under the care of the Poverty Assistance program, which provides free grain to the families of those serving here. We'll even make sure that she gets grain that comes from your mill!"

Amir had a thousand questions, but he was too bewildered to articulate a single one. Instead, he just looked up and said, "Thank you, sir."

Hasec was already halfway out the door. He turned and looked back at Amir. "Thank *you*!" he said, as he nodded his head and exited as abruptly as he'd entered.

·4·
THE GIFT

AFTER HASEC LEFT, one of the guards stayed to explain the daily routine to Amir. Every day would start with a wakeup bell, followed by a bowl of food. After eating, Amir would be required to spend the rest of the morning working on the machine. At some point later in the day, they would deliver a second meal. Then, back to the machine until the third meal, more work, and finally the fourth meal. After that, he could sleep until the morning bell.

As the guard completed the explanation, another

guard delivered the second meal of the day (Amir had already missed the first meal), and Amir was instructed to eat it promptly and get on the machine immediately afterward.

The meal, if it could be called that, was a bowl of boiled cereal grain. It was the same grain that his mother prepared at home, only this one had the warmth, flavor, and consistency of cement. Amir's hunger compelled him to eat, but he was in no hurry, considering the work ahead. After a few hesitant bites, a vigorous knock came at the door.

"Eat up and get on that machine now! I want to hear it humming."

"Yes, sir!" shouted Amir, and he gobbled up the remaining cereal.

He set the bowl and spoon on the floor by the door as he had been instructed and went over to the machine. He got on it as Hasec had demonstrated earlier. He placed his feet on the pedals, his hands on the handles, and started pushing with his feet and pulling with his hands. Somehow, Hasec had made it look easy, though it was actually quite hard. First of all, it took a while to figure out the right order of movement. Then, once he figured that out, the actual working of the machine took a lot of physical effort. At the end of his first working session, he was relieved to hear the bell, even if the only reward was a bowl of cement.

After several hours of tiring work and one more meal, he was very relieved to hear the bell indicating it was time to sleep. The faint lights were extinguished, and the room became so completely black that he could not see his own hand in front of his face. He longed for the relief of sleep, but the stone floor offered him little.

What have I done? he thought to himself as he lay there on the ground, thinking of his poor mother at home, alone, having lost her husband and now her two boys too. *Somehow, someday, I have to make it right. At least my mother is getting some assistance from my work here at The Mill.* It was a cold comfort, but it was all he had.

The next morning Amir awoke to the sound of the bell and the dim lights coming on. Every muscle in his body ached either from the work the previous day, or the stone floor that night. The cold, pasty cereal offered no respite, and his muscles complained with twinges and sharp pains when he remounted the machine. And so passed the second day.

The third day and every day that followed were exactly the same. To say *day* suggests that there was a glimpse of the sun, or a sense of the weather, or a change in season—some indication through sights, sounds, or smells, that a day was beginning or ending. But Amir's only markers were work and sleep.

Without any way to count his days, Amir began taking a little spot of cereal from his first meal of the day and placing it in the corner of his room. Each day he added a new little glob to the perfect little line in the corner. But by the 20th day, it became clear to him that this system simply would not work. Not only did the food deteriorate over time, but on the 20th day, a detachment of ants suddenly arrived to carry off his calendar, one day at a time.

Fortunately, Amir soon discovered he could make

a mark in the mortar between the stones in the wall with the spoon they gave him each morning. He would make one mark between stones every 10 days, and he'd track the days with marks in the mortar above the stones. A two-year sentence meant Amir had 730 days until his release. He slowly circled the room, carefully counting 73 stones over from the stone he had first marked. He identified that as his Freedom Stone. Of course it looked like every other stone, but in his mind that stone started to take on a special aura. He touched it and felt warmth and a sense of hope. After all, he didn't know why others hadn't ever left The Mill, but so far there was no evidence they were keeping him forever. And they didn't show any intention of killing him.

"Maybe they only keep the really bad people. I only stole a chicken, so hopefully they'll let me out in two years."

The next 10 days passed without change, but Amir's 30th morning at the mill began very differently than the rest. The customary bell rang. Then there was a knock on the door, but instead of the food arriving through the slot on the bottom of the door, the door opened! Two guards walked in, one holding the usual bowl of cereal—but this morning, the cereal was adorned with fresh fruit. The second guard held an ornate silver platter, on which rested a small, red silk pillow with beautiful golden trim and tassels at each corner. The pillow looked like it belonged in a palace, not a prison. From the pillow hung a tag, which the guard proceeded to read aloud.

AMIR,

In appreciation of your hard work to support your country and your fellow citizens, I would like to give you this gift. I hope you find that it makes your nights easier and that you awaken each day with a new vigor to continue serving your people.

Thank you,
HASEC
SUPREME COMMANDER
THE MILL

The guard nodded at Amir and pushed the platter toward him.

"Hasec asked me to offer you an apology for not being here himself. He is very pleased with your hard work and wants you to know that you deserve this reward."

"Yes, sir," said Amir, rather surprised. "Uh, thank you, sir."

Then the other guard passed him the bowl of cereal. "Eat up and get to work."

"Yes, sir," nodded Amir as he sheepishly took the bowl in one hand and the pillow in the other. He set the pillow in the corner of the room across from the machine so that he could look at it while he worked. He ate the cereal quickly, then savored the fruit, bite by bite, until the bell rang.

As he slowly got on the machine and started pedaling, pushing, and pulling the levers and pedals, he gazed over at the pillow. He thought of the pillow vendor at the market and closed his eyes to see him more clearly. He thought of all the pillows he had seen over the years, of the big ones fit for a whole family to recline on, of the small ones for ceremonial purposes, of the many colors and fabrics and embellishments, and finally of the man himself. Then he thought of the events of the day in the market that had landed him at The Mill.

He tried to help me. Why didn't I just let him pay for the chicken? How could I be so stubborn?

Then his thoughts turned to the vendor's daughter. He remembered the first time he had seen her. She had been so shy, only peeking at him from behind the table where she was busy embellishing pillows. Over the years he had seen her every week, and every week he had tried to learn more about her. But her father was a private man and always turned the conversation back to pillows. He knew only that her mother had passed away and that she helped her father with the pillow business. As she had matured into a young woman, she had grown quite lovely, but she was still demure and had never said a word to him until that fateful day in the market.

She talked to me. She tried to stop me from making a

fool of myself. But I didn't say anything. I just ran away like the fool that I am. If I had only accepted her father's gift, I would not be stuck here. What was I thinking?

His justification for his actions led him further back in time. *Why did my father have to die? If he hadn't died, everything would be fine.*

He spent the rest of that session feeling sorry for himself and his unfair lot in life. After the second bowl of cereal, he got back on the machine and looked over at the pillow again. Its bright colors and soft edges were a welcome departure from the colorless, cold world of his cell. The pillow happened to be right below the 73rd stone, the Freedom Stone. He decided the pillow was a good sign. Perhaps they were going easy on him because they realized he wasn't a bad person. Other people didn't get out of The Mill because they were bad people who didn't follow the rules. If he followed the rules and worked hard, he'd get out in 700 days and make things right with his mother, his brother, the vendor, and the vendor's daughter. That night Amir put his head on the pillow, thankful for the good sign.

THE NEXT

The NEXT MORNING there was a knock on Amir's door, but this time the door didn't open, the men didn't come in, and there was no gift—just the usual cereal without fruit. Amir ate the cereal, pondering the events of the previous day. His spirits remained high as he thought about the pillow and how well he had slept. He mounted the machine with a sense of pride at working hard to provide for his mother and the people of his country.

But over the following days and weeks, his elevated sense of purpose and his satisfaction with the pillow ebbed. It wasn't that he wasn't thankful for the pillow. He was. But he was growing accustomed to it.

One cool night as he was trying to fall asleep, a thought dripped into Amir's consciousness:

It would be nice to have a blanket.

The thought lingered for a moment, but then something interesting happened. As he lay there with his eyes closed, he could see his father as if he were sitting across from him at home. His father looked at him with warmth in his eyes and said, "I love you, Son. You don't need a blanket." And then the image of his father disappeared. Amir rolled over and thought to himself, *You're right, Father. How could I be so greedy?*

But the seed was sown. The next night the thought occurred to him again, as did the vision of his father and the admonition. From then on, there was not a night in which he did not think about a blanket. And each night the pillow felt smaller, the ground harder, and the air cooler. His father's warning was no less compelling the 10th time than the first, but thoughts of blankets eventually consumed Amir's days as well as his nights. By the 100th thought of a blanket, his father was losing ground. By the 1000th he was not even given a chance.

Finally, one morning it happened. The knock was followed by the opening of the door. Two guards walked in, one with a gift-laden platter and the other with a special breakfast. Amir's eyes were fixed on the bright, beautifully embroidered blanket on the silver platter. He was so consumed and surprised by the fulfillment of his desire that his head was in a fog as the guards acted out their parts: reading the tag, apologizing for Hasec's absence, and encouraging him to eat promptly before getting back to work.

The guard gestured for Amir to take the blanket. So he grabbed it and wrapped it around his shoulders. It immediately took the edge off the cool morning. He inspected it closely, stroking the smooth folds that fell over his shoulders and arms. The breakfast-bearer reminded Amir to take the breakfast and eat before the bell sounded. Awakening from his daze, Amir took his breakfast and offered a feeble "Thank you, sir" as the two guards departed.

That night, as his body cooled down from the heat of his hard work and he began to feel a little chill, Amir wrapped the blanket around himself. It warmed his body, but almost immediately, he saw his father's concerned face. "I love you, Son. You did not need the blanket. Remember what I said, 'The desire for more is insatiable.'"

As he lay down to sleep, Amir thought about his father's words, but he concluded that the blanket really was necessary. Together, a pillow and a blanket were all he needed. It had been 60 days, so he had already served 1/12 of his sentence. It would have been impossible to survive the experience without being able to sleep, and these two items made that possible. They made the experience tolerable. He would not need anything else.

But each day the air grew cooler, the floor harder, the pillow smaller, and the blanket thinner.

At first Amir had slept with the blanket over him to keep him warm, but that didn't address the hardness of the floor. And when he slept with the blanket under him, he was cold all night. So he alternated between sleeping with the blanket under him and sleeping with it over him, but neither was satisfying.

The next thought was inevitable: *What if I had a mat?*

This time, Amir's mind was one step ahead of his father: *I know I thought the pillow and blanket were enough, but I could work harder and be a better servant to my people if I could sleep well. Wouldn't that be better for them?* And suddenly his eyes lit up, and a smile crept across his face. *And for Mother?* That was it! It would be better for his mother. With this irrefutable argument firmly planted in his mind, Amir immediately started fantasizing about a thick sleeping mat.

Hours on the machine melted into days and then weeks, but Amir was not really present. He went through the motions as he contemplated the minutest details of the sleeping mat: It was a handbreadth in thickness, soft enough to comfort his aching body, but firm enough to support him. And most importantly, he would be able to sleep. *It would change everything.* This last detail he considered very thoroughly. Anytime his father threatened to show his face, Amir simply reminded him that a good night sleep would ensure that he'd do a good job and get out of The Mill as soon as possible to get home and support Mama.

Amir had deduced from the pattern of the first two gifts, on the 30th and 60th days of his imprisonment, that the next one would come on the 90th day. As that day approached, his excitement mounted to such extremes that he could hardly sleep.

On the much-anticipated morning, the knock was followed by the entrance of the same two guards, who followed the same script as before—with one exception. Amir was too focused on the thick, rolled mat to notice, but this time they did not make any apology for Hasec's absence. Amir distractedly thanked the men as they left, already wondering what would come on day 120. His body was nearly motionless while he ate his breakfast. He sat quietly on the new mat with the blanket wrapped around his shoulders. But his mind was jumping and running and spinning way ahead of him.

· 6 ·

THE AWAKENING

ALL THAT DAY, Amir could not stop thinking about the new mat and how much better he would sleep that night. Finally, after the last shift, he grabbed the luxurious, thick mat and laid it out, put his pillow at one end, and adjusted the blanket over himself.

At last, he would have a good night's sleep. But as Amir lay down, he felt strangely restless. He was physically more comfortable than ever before, but his soul was not at ease. Since the anticipation of this gift had kept him up all of the previous night, he wondered if he were just too tired. After tossing and turning, he eventually fell into a fitful sleep.

That night, he had a dream. In it, he saw his mother and aunt sitting by the fire, eating bread, and talking. He could not see their faces, and they could not see him. He could see their figures as clearly as if he were in the room, but their voices were distant and muffled. He couldn't get closer to them, and no matter how hard he tried to listen, he could not discern what they were saying.

The next morning he awoke, frustrated and disappointed. The bedding comforted his body physically, but the dream had given him considerable anxiety. Something was wrong, but he couldn't figure out what. He had a pit in his stomach and couldn't eat. The resulting hunger combined with the lack of sleep made the machine work extra exhausting.

That night he dreamt of his mother and aunt again, and again he saw them from the back, but at an angle. He could see their jaws moving as they talked, but not their lips. Their voices were louder now but still muffled and indistinguishable.

On the third night, he saw his mother and aunt again, but this time he could see their faces. They had aged considerably since he last saw his mother in the courthouse. His mother looked more like his grandmother, her face full of sorrow as tears streamed from her eyes. Though their voices were muffled, he could finally hear what they were saying. It was his aunt that was talking, and she was offering condolences to her sister. "It's okay. They're okay. They're in a better place now."

Amir woke up screaming, "Mother! I'm here!"

He was terrified and shaking. Why was his aunt talking as if they were gone forever? His sentence was only two years long.

And then it hit him. It hit him like a goat in the stomach. This was The Mill. No one ever left The Mill. His mind was racing now; images of the past four months flashed through his head. The judge, his mother's face in the courtroom, the rough transport from the jail to The Mill, getting separated from his brother, the machine, Hasec's nod as he left his cell, the guards, the gifts...

The gifts!

The room was pitch black, but in his mind, he began to see the light. These were not gifts at all. They were some kind of trap. With a sense of foreboding, he remembered that each of the gifts had come with a tag attached, and that the guard had read each of the tags as the gifts were delivered. Amir had ripped the tags off, tossed them in a corner of the cell, and forgotten all about them. But now he felt the urgent need to see those tags and read them again for himself. Though the room was so dark that he couldn't see his hand in front of his face, he crawled around until he found each of the tags and stacked them carefully next to his bed.

A tear escaped out of the corner of his eye and rolled to the back of his head as he lay on his pillow and contemplated his fate. What did the tags say? Would they give him a clue to his dream? His head was spinning, and tears continued to roll down his face and onto the pillow. He was scared, too scared to sleep. Or so he thought, until the light rudely awoke him the next morning.

•7•

THE TRUTH

A MIR OPENED HIS EYES with the sense that something terrible had happened, but at first he couldn't remember what it was. It took a moment for him to recall his location and condition. Then he remembered: he was in prison, and he'd had terrible dreams the last three nights in a row. But last night, something had happened.

The tags!

He rolled over immediately and found them sitting in a stack next to the bed. He read the front of the first tag. It was exactly as the guard had read it, but on the back, there was more. It was very small print, and had faded in the past couple of months. He squinted, trying to make out the words. As he read, a cold chill traveled down his spine.

Since you are unable to reimburse us for the cost of providing this reward, you will simply be asked to make up for it with a little extra service. By accepting this reward, you acknowledge the addition of 30 days to your service commitment here at The Mill.

Amir's heart fell into his stomach, and he felt like he was going to throw up. He was dizzy, but he had to see what the other tags said. The second tag had come with the blanket. He went straight to the last sentence:

...By accepting this reward, you acknowledge the addition of 60 days to your service commitment here at The Mill.

He picked up the third tag. He was looking for just one thing now:

...90 days...

At this, Amir retched, but nothing came out. He hadn't eaten his last two meals and had eaten very little in the last three days. He rolled back onto the mat and looked up at the ceiling as the room spun and the floor tilted back and forth. He closed his eyes and quietly uttered a single word out loud.

"Help."

In his mind, he could see his father clearly again. Father was standing, looking right at him. He reached out his hands and grabbed Amir's shoulders. "Son, this truth will set you free."

There was a knock at the door as the guards dropped off his food. Amir didn't think he could eat, but the vision of his father had given him a glimmer of hope. He sat up and tried to eat a little of the food in the bowl while contemplating his circumstances. He added up the days. So far, he had been at The Mill for 93 days, and according to the tags, the gifts had added 30, 60, and 90 days each. He started feeling lightheaded again just thinking of that. But then he closed his eyes and remembered his father's words. He had to press on.

The three gifts had added 180 days to his sentence, and he had only been in for half of that.

So this is how they do it. This is why nobody ever gets out. I hate them! I can't believe they tricked me.

But before he had a chance to go much further down that hole of hatred, the bell went off, and he went over to the machine. While he worked, he thought about the gifts, The Mill, and how much longer he had to stay. His original sentence was 730 days, and now he had just learned that his sentence was lengthened by 180 days. So now he had 817 days left, or two years, two months, and 27 days. Every time he thought about the fact that the remainder of his sentence was longer than when he first entered, anger would build to the point that he'd stop pedaling. But then the bell would go off, reminding him to keep working.

Amir was wishing once again that he had never taken the pillow in the first place when an idea occurred to him: what if he just gave them all back? Then they would have to reduce his sentence back to the original two years. He resolved to do it, and at the next meal break, he gathered the pillow, the blanket, and the mat. The pillow was a little worn after a couple months' use on the stone floor, so Amir tried to clean it up. In fact, it was much worse than a little worn; it was in tatters.

They're not going to take this back.

He was crestfallen, but he decided to try anyway. He set the pillow on the only slightly less worn blanket. At least the sleeping mat, which carried the heaviest price tag, was in pretty good condition. After all, he'd only had it for three days. Surely they'd take that one back! He picked it up and brushed it off, folded it as neatly as possible, and set it on top of the pillow and blanket. He figured it was best to put the nicest-looking piece on top. Maybe that way they'd take all of them without seeing the condition of the bottom two items.

When the time for the last meal of the day came around, Amir waited, carefully listening for footsteps in the hall. As soon as he heard them stop at his door, he called out, "Sir, I have a request!"

A gruff "What?" came back through the door along with the meal.

Amir spoke quickly, using his most friendly and respectful voice, "I wish to return the gifts that—"

"No." The voice came back even gruffer.

"But I didn't realize they would increase my sentence. Now that I know that, I don't want to keep them." It was quiet outside. He couldn't hear any footsteps. Amir called out, "Hello? Are you still there?" Not a sound.

That night, he resolved to keep asking and to try different approaches. Each morning, he folded up the bedding, being extra careful to keep it as clean as possible. At each meal of the day, he tried to communicate his dire need to return the gifts. But after his first attempt, he was no longer acknowledged with so much as a "No." He had no idea if it were the same guard each time or different ones, nor did he know whether they were listening, or if they could even hear him.

After days and days of trying every possible approach with the guards at every meal, he acknowledged that his attempts were not working, and he resigned himself to the fact that his stay would be six months longer than the original two years. But at least now that he knew that the gifts came at a cost, he would know better than to accept the next one.

His anxiety grew as the 120th day approached. What would happen? Would they force him to take the gift? Could he try to give the other gifts back at that time?

The question that haunted him the most was why nobody had ever left The Mill. If he refused the next gift, then he'd be out in a little over two years. But no one had *ever* left The Mill. Did he really have a life sentence? Then why have the tags with days listed? Was it just a ruse to keep people hopeful? Night after night, Amir struggled to sleep, until the eve of the 120th day, when he could not sleep at all.

On the morning of the 120th day, there was a knock at the door. The two guards entered, and the familiar ritual started once again. This time the gift was a sweater. It looked very warm, and Amir had been getting colder over the past few weeks. He reached out to accept it, but then he caught himself and gathered his courage to say, "No, thank you."

They looked at him quizzically.

"Are you sure?" The first guard said, raising one eyebrow. He leaned forward and asked again. "Are you absolutely sure?"

Amir was afraid but said, "Yes."

With that, they turned around and left, taking the sweater with them, before he had a chance to ask about returning his other gifts.

·8·

THE GARDEN

I DID IT! thought Amir. *If I can just say "No" next month, and keep saying "No," I* will *make it out of here.*

He ate his meal. With this relief, he had regained his hunger, and while the meal was far from good, it at least filled his stomach. He spent the rest of the day working and eating, back to his regular routine. After the second meal of the day, he got on the machine and started working through its motions. With a sense of confidence that came from making the right move that morning, he closed his eyes. His father was waiting for him.

"Son, I want to show you something very important."

"Yes, Father," said Amir. His body kept moving, working on the machine, but in his mind, Amir was walking hand in hand with his father toward a high brick wall with an intricately wrought iron gate in the middle of it. Through the closed gate, Amir could see what appeared to be a garden. Together they approached the gate, and his father opened the door and gestured for him to enter.

"Son, this garden is your mind, your heart, and your soul. It is the real you. Your body, your arms, feet, eyes, and mouth are not really you. They are just instruments that allow you to physically represent yourself in the physical world."

Amir stepped in and looked around. It was a handsome structure, and there were some beautiful plants in the garden. There were several young trees, some small hedges, and an immature covering of grass with a lot of bare soil. Off to one side there was a pool, but it, as with much of the garden, was mostly obscured by weeds, thistles, and vines.

"What are all these plants?" asked Amir.

"This garden is the real you. Everything in here is part of who you are," replied his father.

"But there are so many weeds," said Amir.

"That is true, and that is why I brought you here," said his father, as he took Amir's hand and walked him to the center of the garden. In front of them stood two young trees. One tree looked healthy, but the other was almost completely overwhelmed by weeds, thistles, and vines.

"Father, what are these two trees, and why is that one so sick?" asked Amir.

"These are Love and Hope. And as you observed, Hope is under attack." It was a young tree, and nearly all of its branches had been broken. Some of them were gone completely, while others had no leaves or only withered, brown leaves. Only a few branches still showed signs of green life in them despite their wilted leaves. It was not hard to see why the tree was in such poor condition. It was encircled and encumbered by three terrible weeds.

His father led Amir closer to the tree. "These thick, leafy weeds that have filled the soil all around the base of the tree are Tragedies. Notice how they spread their broad leaves over the grass of Self-Control to kill it off. As their leaves wilt, for they don't last long, they leave bare patches of soil, which are fertile ground for those thistles called Indulgences."

He pointed at the vicious-looking thistles that had grown taller than the tree itself. "As these Indulgences grow, their thick stocks get taller and stronger, providing the perfect path for the real killer, the vine of Fantasy. You can see where they have traveled up the stocks of Indulgence and into the branches of Hope," noted his father.

Amir observed the many stalks of thistles and the many vines that had grown up the stalks into the canopy of the tree. There they were smothering the leaves and strangling the branches. There was no doubt that if they continued to grow, they would destroy the tree in little time.

Amir continued to inspect the two trees, then asked, "Father, what are the two flowers I see? They look almost identical, but one is on the tree and the other is on the vine." As he inspected the flowers, he observed that the one in the tree had softer petals with a smooth, delicate scent, while the one in the vine had a brighter stamen and a very strong, sweet smell.

"The flowers in the tree of Hope are Joy," responded his father, "and the ones on the vine of Fantasy are Bliss." As he was speaking, the Bliss flower shriveled up, and the smell changed from sweet to sour. His father continued, "Joy's bloom grows slowly, but it never fades and never wilts unless it is strangled by the vines of Fantasy. Bliss blooms very quickly, and as you've just witnessed, it wilts even faster than it blooms."

Amir took it all in, then exclaimed, "But, Father, it's not my fault. I didn't cause the tragedies. I didn't want you to die. I didn't cause the drought."

His father interrupted him. "Son, that's only partially true. Some tragedies, such as those you mentioned, are completely outside of your control. But you do have control over how you respond to them. If you dwell on them, they grow and spread their leaves to kill Self-Control, which creates an environment in which Indulgences and another cycle of Tragedies are the natural result. For that second set of Tragedies, you must take responsibility."

Amir contemplated his father's wisdom for a moment. "So, I didn't have any control over the drought or the cost of the chicken increasing, but when I indulged in anger and then in stealing the other chicken, I caused the tragedy of getting sent to The Mill."

"Yes, exactly," replied his father. "So you understand."

Amir looked at the tree closely, then asked, "Is Hope dead?"

"What do you think?" replied his father.

"It doesn't look healthy, but it doesn't look dead either. Can it be saved?" asked Amir.

"*That* is the question, Son. That *is* the question," exclaimed his father. "And there is not an easy answer. It is simple but very difficult. In short, you must grow your Self-Control, minimize the effect of the Tragedies when they come, and kill Indulgences and Fantasies."

"Will there still be more Tragedies?" questioned Amir.

"Oh yes, there will always be Tragedies. Some will be the result of your Indulgences, and others will be outside of your control. But they will always come."

"Then how do I deal with them when they come?" shot back Amir.

"By accepting them," said his father.

"But I don't want them!" shouted Amir.

"Nobody does, Son, but you don't have a choice in the matter. They *will* come. If you try to ignore them, their leaves spread, and you magnify their impact. But if you look directly at them and identify them for what they are, then you may clip their leaves and diminish their impact. Mourn a loss, but do not dwell on it. If it is a wrong done to you, forgive the other. If it is a wrong done by you, forgive yourself. A strong ground cover of Self-Control will help."

"Then how do I grow Self-Control?" asked Amir.

"Slowly, by rejecting the Indulgences and Fantasies. Every time you say 'No' to an Indulgence or a Fantasy, your Self-Control grows stronger."

"But how do I say 'No' when Bliss smells so good?" asked Amir.

"By saying 'Yes' to something better," responded his father. "Behind every strong 'No,' there is a stronger 'Yes.' You must find your stronger 'Yes.'"

The delivery of the third meal abruptly shook Amir from his vision. As he ate, Amir thought about the garden he had seen and about his father's words. *What is my stronger "Yes"?* For the first time since his incarceration began, he looked beyond The Mill. He tentatively leaned on the little Hope that he had left. *Is there life after the Mill? Is it possible they will honor my rejection of the fourth gift? Will I get out? What will I do when I get out? Of course, I'll go to see my mother, and...*

Then suddenly a thought occurred to him: *What*

about Mamluk? Had he received a pillow too? Did he take it? Of course he took it! He's too young to know otherwise. If I took it, surely he took it. What about the blanket, and the mat, and the sweater? He probably took all of them, and he probably doesn't know about the cost. He will have already doubled his sentence!

This string of thoughts threatened to suck him into a vortex of pain, anger, and shame, but he recognized it for what it was: a Tragedy. He chose to accept it and clip its leaves. He concluded that if he could get out, his brother could get out too. It might take him longer to figure out the trick of the gifts, but as long as he figured it out in the next two months, he could still get out before Amir.

Amir strengthened his bed of Self-Control. He started to think about what his life would hold for him. One thing he knew for sure: no matter how dire his circumstances, he would never again take a shortcut like stealing the chicken. He yearned to be like his father: to marry a lovely woman like his mother, have children, and raise them in a warm home. He wanted to buy the land that his father had talked about. Amir dreamed of working hard, saving his money, and buying the land so that his mother and brother and family could all live and work and reap what they'd sown. With those comforting thoughts, he drifted off to sleep on day 120.

•9•
THE CALCULATION

The NEXT MORNING, the guards opened Amir's door for the first meal. His chest tightened up and he swallowed a lump in his throat when he saw what they had with them: the sweater.

"We offer you another chance to take your gift," said one of the guards. Amir shuddered at the smirk on the guard's face.

Then, with a swell of confidence from the previous day's dreams, Amir said, "No, I do not want it," and then, remembering, he added, "I want to return my other gifts too."

"Return the gifts?" said the guard. "No."

"I do not want them, and they are not really gifts anyway," said Amir.

The guard interrupted, "I don't know what you are talking about, but no one has ever returned a gift. It is not permissible. Once you have accepted one, you may not return it."

With that, the guards turned and left the room.

Amir's sunny attitude from the previous day was now clouded by frustration. Not only had they explicitly rejected his request to return the gifts, but there was a new twist. It would be one thing to reject the offering once every 30 days, but it would be another altogether to reject a gift every single day.

His fears were confirmed when the guards returned with the gift the next morning, and the morning after that, and the next, and so on for several more days. Each day the routine was the same, until on the seventh day they changed it.

"We have a special offer for you," said one guard.

"What are you talking about?" replied Amir.

"Well, you have done such a good job of working the machine that The Mill's production has gone up, so you may have this gift for only 90 days," explained the guard.

"90 days?" For a moment, Amir was puzzled, but then he understood. If the previous gifts demonstrated any kind of trend, this gift probably had a 120-day cost, but they were offering it to him for a cost of only 90 days. "Hmm, 90 days. No, thank you." And they left.

On the next day, the guard announced, "You are evidently doing a tremendous job because they instructed me to give this to you for just 60 days." And then he did something that puzzled Amir. He leaned in close and half-whispered into his ear, "I can only imagine what they'll offer you tomorrow." And with a wink, he turned and departed.

Left alone, Amir felt confused. Why the wink? What did the guard mean by his statement? Why did he whisper it? It was loud enough for the other guard to hear.

He thought about what had just happened as he finished his meal and got on the machine. *He did not even give me a chance to say, "No,"* thought Amir to himself. *Maybe he didn't give me a chance to say "Yes," because tomorrow he will offer an even better deal! But why? Anyway, he is giving me a deal, and he did not have to. It's probably going to be the sweater for only 30 days. That is a pretty good deal. It is getting colder, and I will need a sweater.*

The air in the cell felt cooler, and Amir began to imagine how much more comfortable he would be with the sweater. Just then, the second meal was brought to his room, and he was awoken from his fantasy of warmth and comfort. In his mind, he saw his father looking at him with love and concern in his eyes. "Son, remember Bliss."

"Yes, I know Father. It does not last."

"No, my son, it is worse. It is the bloom of Fantasy, which kills Hope!"

He ate the meal, reflecting on his father's wisdom, and got back on the machine. "The more stuff I get, the less of me there is. I shouldn't get that sweater. But I'm cold and miserable, and it's the only thing I need. After that, I know I will not need anything else."

Then the calculation began. "30 days is nothing compared to the more than 600 days I have left. I'll pay just $1/20^{th}$ of the total in exchange for all the benefit of having a warm sweater for that entire time. That's worth it."

$$\maltese$$

The next day, the guards entered and offered the sweater to Amir. "Only 45 days," said one guard with a smile.

"But I thought it would be 30," complained Amir.

The guard responded quickly, "It's 45, and tomorrow it will be back to 60. Do you want it or not?"

Amir hesitated, and the guards turned to leave.

"I want it!" Amir shouted.

"Very well. Here it is. You won't regret it." Then the guards turned to leave.

•10•

THE LOOP

The VERY SECOND the sweater touched Amir's hands, he was overwhelmed with regret. For a split-second, he stared down at it in disgust and shame, and then he lunged after the guards as they exited.

"I don't want it. Take it back!" Amir shouted, thrusting the sweater toward the guards. They turned, and yanked the door. Amir was leaning forward and his head was knocked by the door flying shut.

He awoke, dazed, with a terrible headache. He didn't know what time it was, but there was uneaten food in a bowl on the floor and the bell was going off, telling him to get on the machine and get to work. He slowly got up, feeling very tired and dizzy, and got to work on the machine.

The sweater was on the floor next to the pillow, the blanket, and the mat. Amir was chilled, but he could not bear the thought of wearing the sweater. He resolved to never wear the sweater. In fact, he would set it in the corner to remind him not to accept any other gifts. With this resolution, he felt a new sense of confidence that carried him through the day.

The next morning, the guards did not enter. Amir did not bother to try to return the sweater or argue with them because by now he knew that pursuit was fruitless. After eating, he went over to the sweater, picked it up, and folded it neatly. He then propped it up against the wall next to the door. "Every time those guards come through this door, I am going to look at this sweater and be reminded not to take any gift they may offer."

The next several days passed without incident. As

the 150th day drew nearer, his anxiety grew. What would they try next? So far, he had fallen for every gift they had offered. One way or another, he was *not* going to fall for this one. He asked his father for wisdom and the confidence to say "No" to whatever temptation came his way.

On the morning of the 150th day, the guards entered and enacted the familiar ritual. On the platter they offered a pair of warm-looking pants. Amir's mind flashed to the warmth he would experience wearing those pants, but instantly he put it out of his mind and rejected the offer. The guards promptly left.

As he ate the meal, he considered the most recent gift. If he were really cold, he could wear the sweater, and since he had already committed to not wearing it, the pants were relatively easy to reject. *I wonder how much they want for them,* he thought. But then he realized that even wondering this opened the door to calculating the value at which he would accept them, as he had done with the sweater. He did not want to fall into that trap, so he decided that he didn't care how much they wanted for the pants. But still, he wondered.

He knew they would bring the pants again the next day, but would they do anything else to tempt him to accept them? Amir couldn't think of anything all that compelling. *I guess this one won't be too hard to avoid,* he decided when it occurred to him that eventually they would switch gifts if he rejected one long enough. This thought put him in a sour mood because he knew sooner or later they'd come up with something truly tempting and harder to resist.

The next day, they brought the pants again, and again he rejected them. This scene was repeated for the next several days, weeks in fact. They never changed their tone, offered a different price, or modified any aspect of the presentation. It was exactly the same, day after day. Amir was surprised that they did not try a new approach or change gifts on him, but he was also happy that they didn't because he was already resolved not to accept the pants. He knew that every day he did not accept them, he was another day closer to getting out.

One day as Amir was eating the tasteless slop they fed him every day, he remembered a particularly tasty meal his mother had prepared for his 16th birthday. Every year for his birthday she offered to make whatever he wanted. In principle, she was offering to make anything, but every year since Amir could remember, he had asked for the same thing: her superb lamb stew. They only had it on special occasions, and it was his favorite meal. "It is the dish of royalty," his mother would always say, and he agreed wholeheartedly.

She would send Amir to buy a leg of lamb from the butcher at the market, and then she would sear it in a pan until each side was dark brown and the whole house was filled with the warm, rich aroma. Then she would add some water and cut vegetables, a few minced herbs, and some dried spices that were stored away for special occasions. She would move the pan to the edge of the fire and let it cook all day. At night, the family and the guests that always showed up on special occasions gathered around the pot to remove the top. The aroma filled the air as his mother served out the soup until there was just one serving left. The last, best, juiciest serving went into a dish for Amir, and he savored every bite.

The memory was so vivid he could almost feel the tender bits of lamb succumbing to his teeth and the broth washing across his tongue and down his throat. He felt the warm bread in his hand, its aroma wafting up into his nostrils. He heard the bread's crust shatter before he dipped it into the soup and brought the dripping piece to his mouth.

The buzzer rudely interrupted his dream and reminded him to get up from his slop and get on the machine. He decided that when he got out he would raise lambs so that his mother could make her special stew every week and share it with their friends and neighbors.

Over the course of the next few days, the guards continued to present the pants every morning, and Amir could not stop thinking about that spectacular meal by his mother. He remembered variations on the stew, the different types of bread she had made, and the friends who had joined them on various special occasions.

Day 189 started just like every other, but it ended quite differently. At the third break of the day, about the time that the food should have been left under his door, he heard sounds outside, and his door opened. A foreign smell wafted into the room with the opening of the door. And yet it was not foreign at all. It was the smell of his mother's stew. Not the smell of a stew *like* his mother's, but the *exact* smell of it. The same one he asked for every birthday.

"Today is your birthday. So we asked your mother what she'd like to give her son, and she said this is your favorite stew. So we had her make a batch for you. I hope you enjoy it," said the first guard as he handed the bowl to Amir.

Amir studied the stew for a moment and knew it was hers. He took the bowl from the guard's hands, and the guards backed through the door and disappeared. The look on their faces was all he needed.

•11•
THE END

EFEATED, AMIR SAT DOWN. He bit his lip and slowly breathed in while he felt his back, neck, and arms tense. His eyes filled with tears, and with a faint whimper, he began to cry. He sat on the floor with his mother's bowl of stew in his lap while he rocked back and forth. It was the first time he had allowed himself to really cry since he lost his father.

A little vine of Fear crept through his garden, and he felt it growing stronger. Fear ran up his spine and snaked around his arms. His fingers tingled as he thought, *Will I ever get out of here*?

"Not if you keep failing like this," said a voice back to him.

This was not his father's voice. It was his uncle, whom he could now see as clearly as if he were standing there. He was looking down at Amir with disdain and disgust.

"How could you be so stupid? You know how it works in here. What were you thinking, that they would change the rules for you because it's your birthday? You were your father's only hope for your mother, and now she has nothing left but me."

Amir closed his eyes tightly, but his uncle would not go away. He continued to assault Amir until at last the buzzer went off, reminding Amir to get to work. The vision disappeared, but he could not bring himself to get up. He just sat there frozen, the stew growing cold in his lap.

Suddenly, the guards burst into the room, grabbed Amir by the arms and picked him up off the floor. As they jerked him to his feet, the bowl flew out of the cradle of his lap. It flipped through the air and shattered on the floor. Bits of stew and broken pottery flew everywhere. And on the broken bottom of the bowl, Amir could make out three numbers painted carefully inside.

1 2 0

This was a confirmation of his fear, but it was better knowing than fearing. He stood up straight, shook himself, and informed the guards that he would get on the machine himself.

"Do not let that happen again," said one guard. "We won't be as pleasant next time."

When the shift was over, Amir got off the machine and lay down. At first, he was too agitated to sleep, and he started to dwell on his uncle's comments. But as his mind started to wind up with fear, fatigue from the day overcame his body, and he fell into a fitful sleep. During the night he was awoken several times by mice crawling around and over him as they consumed his mother's gift. But he was too tired to bother with them.

The next morning, when the lights and food woke him, Amir got up slowly and ate his first meal. He had a terrible headache to match his considerable body aches, but those were mere physical pains and did not compare to the aching of his heart. Amir had grown up in a loving family with a community around him. He had always felt like he was a part of something bigger than himself. This morning, he felt apart from anything or anyone. Alone.

He also had the overwhelming sense that his situation was entirely his fault. The echoes of his uncle's voice agreed.

Amir closed his eyes and saw his father. "Son, know first that I love you. Nothing you do can take that away. Nothing. Second, know that your story is not finished. In fact, it has only just begun. You are young and have many years ahead of you. I know that you will not just survive, but thrive, and the lessons you learn here will shape your life in powerful ways. Everyone falls. The question is: What will you learn from falling, and how will you rise?"

Amir rose from his first meal and mounted the machine. Throughout the day, he ruminated on the encouragement of his father and the derision of his uncle. One moment he felt hopeful and alive; the next, he was overwhelmed with shame. In the blink of an eye, he could revert from one state to the other.

Why, he thought to himself, *am I so fickle?* He couldn't answer the question, but he decided that if he could pass so quickly from hope to shame, he could just as easily move from shame back to hope. This was a comfort, albeit a small one.

At this point, Amir's total sentence amounted to nearly three years, and he was only six months into it. Over the ensuing days, weeks and months, he was continually assaulted by offers from the guards. For the most part, he stood firm. But every once in a while, his will gave way, and he accepted an offer. Whenever this happened Amir would immediately feel overwhelmed with guilt and shame. At these times, his uncle's voice was always right there with him.

"You did it again."

"Who are you kidding?"

"I knew you couldn't handle it."

"What makes you think you are so special?"

On a couple occasions, he started to cry, and his uncle pounced on him, "Are you serious? What are you, a baby? I'm embarrassed to even be related to you." After that, Amir stopped crying. If he failed, he failed, but he wasn't going to cry about it.

One time, he accepted three gifts three days in a row. The first one was a piece of fruit. The moment he accepted it, he immediately felt a sense of shame for his weakness. But this time his uncle's voice suggested that he might as well enjoy it. He said that since the fruit only came with a seven-day penalty, it wasn't that bad, and fruit would, after all, help him stay healthy. Amir was shocked when, after licking the last drop of juice from his fingers, he heard his uncle's voice sneer, "Isn't that just like you?"

Furious, Amir shouted every vulgar and obscene word he could muster, glaring into his uncle's face, which he could see very clearly. But his uncle just snickered at him.

Amir went to bed that night full of anger, only to wake up the next morning to face the same offer.

While a voice inside cried, "NO!", Amir's hand reached out and took the fruit. As he acknowledged what he had done, he went into a fog of shame, hatred, and self-loathing so intense that he was not surprised when he accepted the same offer on the third day. As usual, his uncle started to attack him, but before he had finished his first word, Amir summoned the courage to say one word, "No." His uncle was silenced.

Then Amir closed his eyes and quietly asked, "Father. What do I do?"

He saw his father looking at him with determination in his eyes. "You know what I'm going to say."

"That you love me," said Amir.

"And?" his father added.

"That nothing I can do will change that."

"Exactly."

"But how will that stop me from taking another piece of fruit tomorrow or another gift on any other day?"

"The power to reject the fruit and every other gift they present to you is not your will. There is a power greater and deeper than your will. It is love. You need to fully love yourself first. You will have the power to fully love yourself, regardless of anything you do, when you accept that I fully love you regardless of anything you do. Anger breeds failure, failure breeds shame, and shame breeds anger. It's a vicious cycle that will pull your garden apart. But, Son, love breeds hope, and hope breeds will, and with will comes freedom."

"Thank you, Father, for loving me. But I can't love myself. I keep messing up."

"Son, your love for yourself, or anyone else, cannot be sustained by actions—yours or anyone else's. Actions are like a breeze that comes and goes without warning. You and others will always disappoint you. But love is sustained by love."

Amir had an idea, but the lights were out now; it would have to wait until the next day.

•12•

THE BEGINNING

The NEXT MORNING the guards walked in with a new piece of fruit. Amir looked at the guards and said, "No, thank you."

Once the guards left, he walked over to the sweater and examined its bottom edge. He searched patiently until he found the end of the yarn, and he untied the knot that kept it in place. Then he unraveled the sweater and wrapped its yarn around his knees. Slowly the sweater ceased to exist as the coil of yarn grew and grew. As he unraveled the sweater, he sang a song his mother had taught him as a small child.

There are so many opportunities,
So many opportunities,
So many opportunities for me to be,
A baker kneading a loaf of bread,
A scribe tracking what's been said,
A groomsman waiting to be wed,
Or a beekeeper with bees.
There are so many opportunities for me.

His mother would make up new verses for the song and sing it to him and Mamluk at night as they were falling asleep. It had been many years since she had sung that song.

As Amir finished unraveling the sweater, the bell notified him that it was time to work. At the next break, he took one end of the yarn in his hand and tied a little knot. Then he tied another knot about a fingernail's length from the first, and a third that much further, and so on until he had tied nine knots. For the tenth, he tied a double square knot that stuck out just a bit further than the others, just enough to be felt if he pulled the yarn through his fingers.

He continued the pattern during the rest of his breaks until he had created a knot for every day of his incarceration: past, present, and future. At the end of the day, he picked up the makeshift yarn calendar, took the end that represented the beginning of his stay at The Mill, and tied it loosely to the spot on the yarn that represented today. He then took the other end of yarn, the end that represented the last day of his sentence, and tied it loosely to the same spot representing today.

The second loop was much bigger than the first, but Amir imagined a day when the loops would be equal, and then a day when the second loop would be tiny, and then gone. On that day, he would walk out of The Mill, free. He would go straight to his mother, put his arms around her, and apologize. Then he would go to the pillow vendor and his daughter and apologize to them and thank them for their attempt to help him.

Amir knelt down, closed his eyes, folded his hands, and asked his father for wisdom. He spoke confidently and out loud, "Father, I know this is going to be hard. I know they will never give up trying to feed my desire for more. I know that anger breeds failure, and failure breeds shame, and shame breeds anger. I also know that the desire for more is insatiable and that the more I feed it, the more it consumes me. I want my *self* back. So I am going to starve that beastly Indulgence, and love myself the way you love me!"

He got up, picked up his pillow, and set it on the floor against the wall. Then he returned for the blanket. He picked it up and folded it neatly into a triangle, as he'd seen the blanket lady do at the market. He tucked the last bit into the triangle and set it next to the pillow so that it was propped against the wall, looking back at him. Lastly, he picked up the mat. He folded it into three sections and set it on the ground next to the other two. Then he decided to put the pillow and the triangle of the blanket on top of the folded mat. Lastly, he laid the calendar rope in front of the gifts.

Then Amir said out loud, "I do not need a pillow. I do not need a blanket. And I do not need a mat. I want all of these things, and I will have a nicer pillow, a nicer blanket, and a real mattress when I get out of The Mill. But right here, right now, these millstones are preventing me from getting out. I love myself enough to live without them for now."

Again, he knelt down and spoke out loud, "Father, I cannot do this without you. I will let these false gifts sit as a reminder to me that if I take any others, it will only lengthen my stay. I'll put the calendar in front of them so that if I'm ever tempted to take one of them, I'll first remember the impact of doing so."

Then he lay down on the hard, stone floor, put his head on his arm, and fell into a deep and comforting sleep. He dreamed of running through an open field of grasses and flowers. They were many shades of green and red and pink and orange and yellow and blue, and they all swayed in waves with the wind. He could feel the sun's heat reaching across the great expanse of the sky to warm his head and back. He held out his hands as he ran through the grass and felt the gentle blades and petals brush against his fingers.

He came to a lake and, without hesitating, jumped in. As he swam around, Amir felt the cool, fresh water flow over his body. Then he stopped swimming, took a breath, and allowed himself to sink into the depths of the lake. He could feel bubbles coming out of his clothing and crawling along his skin, making their way to the surface. He opened his eyes and saw the shafts of sunlight piercing the water. But, suddenly, the sunlight was gone, and the water grew dark while little bubbles rippled the surface. With a stroke of his arms, he surfaced to feel the heavy raindrops pounding his head.

As he walked up out of the lake, he marveled at the dark grey, purple, and black clouds as they piled up above him and poured themselves out onto the welcoming land below. The trees around the lake leaned back as the warm wind grew stronger. Suddenly, a flash of lightning exploded from a cloud into the tallest, strongest, proudest tree on the far side of the lake. The massive tree was split from top to bottom and came crashing down: one side into the lake and the other into the forest behind it, taking two other trees down as it fell. The wind grew stronger still, pushing the clouds and rain into the setting sun before dying down entirely.

In the stillness, Amir lay back in the grass and watched as the oranges and pinks evaporated from the sky, leaving only an inky, black expanse dotted with bright stars and a silver moon. He fell asleep there in the grass, counting the stars.

The next morning, Amir woke up feeling strong and refreshed. He was lying on his back with his arms behind his head. Before arising, he said out loud, "Thank you."

In the garden of his soul, Hope was now strong and tall and true. He went over to the calendar, moved the tied ends over one day and said out loud, "Today, and every day, I will take one step closer to freedom. It will be hard. And there will be many temptations. But a lifetime of freedom is worth two years of suffering.

Thank you, Father, for giving me the strength to suffer now so that I can live later. Give me eyes to see the gifts for what they really are."

He ate his food and worked on the machine through that day, and through the next day and the next. They continued to bring him many gifts: fruits and meats, and sofas and beds, and ice, and offers of days off, and clothing, and sweet flowers—everything you could imagine, and many things you could not. But Amir did not see the gifts for what they appeared to be. Instead he saw only what they represented. Instead of fruits and meats, he saw a pile of dung on a platter. The sofa and bed looked to him like a cage. The ice looked like shackles, the days off like an anchor, the clothing like chains, and the flowers like thorns. His father's spirit had given him eyes to see the truth.

Days passed, then weeks, then months, and eventually he reached the midway mark on his calendar. He celebrated the event by fasting from the little food they gave him each day. His body was hungry, but his soul was satisfied. Rejoicing in starving the insatiable weed,

Indulgence, Amir said, "Father, thank you for giving me the power to say 'Yes' to my future and 'No' to my present." From that day forward, he decided to fast on every tenth day as a reminder to keep his self and starve the desire to indulge.

As Amir practiced his daily ritual of acknowledging his own weakness and failures, and giving thanks for the wisdom and strength of his father, he learned to love himself. His vision became clearer, and his will grew stronger. He slept well at night—not because he was comfortable, but because his soul was on the right path.

Time passed, and the second loop of the yarn calendar got smaller and smaller, until there were only seven days left. Amir decided to fast the last seven days to avoid the temptation of taking a single thing at this moment of truth. Physically, he was wasting away, but his garden was alive and vibrant. In these final days, the desperate guards brought him every possible temptation with every single meal. But it wasn't a fair fight, for Amir did not see as the guards saw. He awoke each morning, knelt by the calendar, adjusted the day, said his "Thank yous," and solicited help from his father. He then mounted the machine and worked until the end of the day, at which point he repeated his "Thank yous," and went to sleep.

On the last night he did not sleep, but knelt at the calendar all night, thanking his father.

The next morning, the guards entered the room with Hasec, whom he had not seen since his very first day at The Mill. Amir stayed kneeling for a moment, then slowly stood up and looked directly into Hasec's eyes. Hasec recoiled slightly and took a half step back.

"So, it's you," said Hasec.

As Amir leaned down to grab the calendar, he felt faint and started to fall over. He steadied himself with his right hand on the wall above the pillow, the blanket, and the mat. He picked up the calendar in his left hand, took one last look at the three gifts, pushed off the wall, and slowly stood back up.

Hasec turned and stepped out the door, and one of the guards followed him. The other motioned for

Amir to follow, and they walked down the long door-lined corridor. Amir's heart was heavy with knowledge of what lay hidden behind each of those doors. They opened a door into a narrow stairwell, and when Amir looked down, he could see more floors than he could count. He looked up and saw just as many more. They descended two flights and opened a door to another hallway that looked like all the rest. After more turns and halls, they came to a door that stood wide open with a guard standing outside of it.

Hasec turned just as he passed the open door and looked back at Amir with a smug look of satisfaction and an ugly smile. By now, Amir had guessed what he was about to see and his stomach was full of knots. But still he was not prepared for its impact. Inside the room, there was a rich rug, a sofa, a bed with linens and pillows, and a table set with fresh fruit, a glass of wine, and a plate of meat and vegetables. There were tapestries on the wall, and candles provided extra light, comfort, and warmth.

Hasec spoke, "All of this could have been yours."

And then Amir saw him.

In the corner of the room, Mamluk was on the machine. His body looked healthy and strong, but his eyes were vacant, staring into space as his body went through the motions of the machine.

Amir had big lump in his throat but managed to shout out, "Mamluk!"

His brother, with a quizzical look on his face, lifted his head to look out the door. Mamluk's eyes met Amir's just in time for the door to slam shut with a thud.

Amir shouted out, "Don't take another one! Don't take any more—"

He was cut off when one of the guards grabbed him from behind and covered his mouth.

"Your brother now lives in comfort and luxury, while you return to nothing," said Hasec with disgust as he turned and continued up the corridor.

Amir continued to struggle with the guards, but his weak, malnourished body was no match for them. They wound their way through the maze of narrow corridors until they came to a wider hall that led to a set of two doors. As they approached, the two doors opened from the outside, and sunlight poured in, illuminating every little speck of dust in its way.

As Amir approached the door, he squinted as his eyes adjusted to the brightness outside.

Hasec had a final word for him: "You'll be back."

As the guards threw him out through the doors, Amir turned to look at Hasec and replied, "Just watch."

ACKNOWLEDGMENTS

It's been a long road, and I have many people to thank for their support throughout the process, but I'll start with, Nienke Schuler, the woman that bled red all over an early draft. I had written about half of the book when I sent her a copy and asked her to hold nothing back. Three pens later, she handed me the draft, and I knew I wanted her on my team. I must also thank Hugh Williams and Priya O'Keefe who both offered significant and tremendously helpful editorial feedback on my first full draft as well.

How can we judge a book without a cover? For the amazing cover art, interior drawings and more, I have to thank the very talented James Bernardin. Also, Randy Kuckuck, and his colleagues at PublishNext, who sat through infinite questions from a new author with lots of business and project management experience, but no book writing experience.

I raised a substantial portion of the funds needed for the initial printing through a successful Kickstarter project. Thank you to the skilled eyes and editorial wizardry of Sam McJunkin for making the video and shooting the author profile photos, to Alathea Pippinger for expertly holding a boom mike for several hours on a Sunday afternoon, to Cindy Ward for being my chief Facebook fan from beginning to end and beyond, and to all of the 175 people that made my project a success.

There are two books on writing that gave me real encouragement to start and then to finish this project: Pat Walsh's "78 Reasons Why Your Book May Never Be Published & 14 Reasons Why It Just Might" was an awesome eye opener. Especially reason #1. Stephen King's "On Writing" was a huge help to me when I was at the halfway point and starting to run out of steam. If you are considering writing a book, I insist on both of these.

Not long after I started writing, I got an intelligent,

young, and energetic high school student to intern for me. Megan Duncan has stuck with me through high school and now into college. Huge thanks to her for nuts and bolts help on everything from database administration, to marketing design, to website setup and much, much more. Thanks also to Campbell Hawk and Mark Smith for their help as interns on this project.

Lastly, thank you to my wife for listening to my first versions of the story while we trained for the Seattle to Portland Bike Ride, and thank you to my sweet little girl who doesn't remember a time when I wasn't working on this book. I hope she reads it and heeds it.

ABOUT THE AUTHOR

Mark D. Bullard is somewhere between a Jack of all Trades and a Renaissance Man. A proud Washingtonian who was actually born in California, he barely got into Cornell University, but graduated in three and a half years. By the age of 18, he had already worked in a print shop, four restaurants, an auto detailer, a boat detailer, a landscaping company, and even got a Hollywood acting gig.

Since Cornell, he has worked in a big hotel in Dallas, a little consulting firm in Seattle, a real estate developer in San Francisco, and a community college in rural North Carolina. The only contiguous string in his resume is software. He has worked at five software companies having from 2 employees to 90,000 in roles as diverse as tech support, partner development, new market evangelist, project manager, VP of Sales, and founder.

He has started a few businesses, been fired at least once, and at one particularly low point, he was rejected by Walmart for a cashier position.

Mark lives on an island near Seattle where he and his delightful wife and daughter maintain a mini-farm with eight chickens, a couple lambs, and one very proficient cat.

He would love to hear your story. You can reach him in a number of ways:

Email:

Mark@nomorepillows.com

Facebook:

https://www.facebook.com/AuthorMarkDBullard

Twitter:

@MarkDBullard

Blog:

http://markdbullard.com/

NO MORE PILLOWS

Has this story struck a chord for you? Can you relate to Amir? While this story is pure fiction, it is in many ways an autobiography of my own life. Though I'm not completely free yet, I have experienced some freedom and would love to be a catalyst to help others do the same. To that end, I have created a community called No More Pillows (http://nomorepillows.com) where people may come together to share their stories, their successes, their failures, their hopes, and their dreams. Please visit us there and share your story or come to be inspired by others. Remember that no matter where you are in your journey, there is always someone ahead of you to encourage you along, and someone behind you looking to you for encouragement.

If you witness examples of "pillows" in your world, share them with this **#nomorepillows** tag on Twitter, Facebook, Instagram, and whatever else is hot by the time you read this.

Lastly, if you would like to have me speak to your book club, community group, anonymous group, support group, school group or any other club, group or organization, please contact me directly at Mark@pfypc.com. If I can't make it in person, I would be glad to speak to your group remotely.

Upward and Onward,
Mark D. Bullard